All Dog Wants for Christmas

Dogs Talk to Santa

Lizz Brady

Illustrations by Alisa Harris

MJF BOOKS
New York

Published by MJF Books
Fine Communications
322 Eighth Avenue
New York, NY 10001

All Dog Wants for Christmas
LC Control Number: 2015909753
ISBN 978-1-60671-314-3

Copyright © 2015 by Lizz Brady

Printed in the United States of America.

Designed by Lisa Chovnick
Illustrations by Alisa Harris

MJF Books and the MJF colophon are trademarks
of Fine Creative Media, Inc.

QF 10 9 8 7 6 5 4 3 2 1

FOR CORY AND MAMA

Santa!!

Hi, hello, hi, hi, hi!

I thought I'd never see you again! I've missed you so much!

I can't believe it's been a whole year since you last visited! I'd like to say that I've been waiting patiently for your return, but HA!, we both know that's a lie! I have so much to catch you up on! I—

Oh. Oh, dear.

I am so, so sorry. This happens sometimes. Oh, geez.

There's a washer/dryer down the hall. Do you mind hanging around for a few hours while I throw your suit in? Don't be embarrassed, Santa; gosh, *I'm* embarrassed! So embarrassed! I'll just be cringing under a blanket while we wait. Here's one for you, too—I'm sure it's a bit drafty.

Lucy

Dear Santa,

Last Christmas there seemed to be a bit of gift confusion: Some of the presents under the tree had names on them other than mine.

I'm sure since you are a busy guy you were probably just flustered and made a mistake. I forgive you, but please don't let it happen this Christmas, okay?

Sincerely,
Maddie

Dear Santa,

I have done my research. For maximum adorability, I would gladly accept the following for a new best friend and possible sidekick for a harrowing cross-country road trip: orangutan, elephant, capuchin, bunny, giraffe, grizzly bear, cockatoo, tiger, and fox.

In fact, feel free to bring me pretty much any animal. Oh, except for a cat—it's been done to death.

Thank you,
Rudy

DEAR SANTA,

BALLOOOOOOOOOOOOOOOOOOOOOOOOONS!
   Balloons, balloons, balloons, balloons.
BALLOONS!

Love,
Taco

P.S. BALLOONS!

DEAR SANTA,

Apparently not every piece of paper that falls through the slot in the door is "junk." How am I supposed to tell what can and can't be chewed?

Anyway, it'd be great if you could give us some replacement "gift cards" and "bonus checks" this Christmas, whatever that means.

Your friend,
Punky

DEAR SANTA,

Last Christmas I had very high hopes for the bottle of eau de toilette you brought us. My French might be a little spotty, but that last word's a no-brainer.

The fancy packaging made me a bit suspicious, true. I also wondered why my human unkindly placed the bottle on a shelf. I had no trouble knocking it down after a few leaps—but it *may* have accidentally shattered.

The next thing I knew, not only was I yelled at and sent to a time-out, but I had the WORST taste in my mouth. Blech!

I don't know what sorts of toilets French people drink out of, and I don't want to sound closed-minded . . . but this Christmas can we please stick to the water from the American kind? Thanks.

Sincerely,
Ernie

Dear Santa,

I look forward to seeing you on Christmas, but please don't be offended if I decline to "shake hands."

I'm a bit of a germophobe, and I would bet my jerky that you and your elves were too busy to get flu shots this year.

> Thank you for understanding,
> Prufrock

Hi Santa,

Care to make a friendly wager? If I can fit four tennis balls in my mouth at the same time, I get dibs on all the presents.

Don't pretend it's a sight you could pass up, Santa!

Athena

DEAR SANTA,

How was I supposed to know THAT tree wasn't for peeing on? Some light bulbs and knickknacks on the branches were supposed to tip me off?

Honestly, I can't keep up with all the rules around here. Please bring us another one before the humans really flip their lids.

Thanks,
Bob

DEAR SANTA,

It deeply saddens me to report that the cat is not being his best self.

I've tried everything I can think of to promote personal growth. I smile at him, but he scowls back. I shout encouragement; he hisses in retort. I nudge him to get on his feet and exercise for once in his crummy little life (sorry—that's the anger talking), and my nose gets scratched. And when I lose my temper and try to defend myself, the humans send ME to a time-out to "relax" while he smirks.

Fortunately, I watch a variety of daytime talk shows. If my gentle life coaching won't get him to shape up and fly right, a screaming drill sergeant at one of those scared-straight boot camps—preferably one in a different time zone—should do the job beautifully.

Every day is a gift,
Charlie

Hɪ Sᴀɴᴛᴀ,

Who's a good boy? WHO'S A GOOD BOY?
     Asking for a . . . friend.

Clyde

Dear Santa,

For Christmas, please bring me my own TV that shows nothing but cartoons. The TV my humans watch blares all sorts of junk that's rotting their brains.

I guess I just have higher standards.

Thank you,
Hazel

Dear Santa,

Spaghetti and meatballs in an alley are great for those fancy Hollywood types, but my lady and I are more "salt of the earth" . . . when we can find it.

If you could bring us a big bag of lawn trimmings or drop us off at the nearest grassy meadow, I assure you we'd be just as content.

Sincerely,
Fred

DEAR SANTA,

This Christmas I would *not* like another Frisbee, unless you also bring my human a football. That way we can both feel inadequate.

Best,
Cliff

DEAR SANTA,

For Christmas I have some weather-related requests. Is this your department? If not, could you forward to the appropriate party?

1) I'm preaching to the choir here, but keep the snow coming! It's so much fun to play in! I'm also getting great at turning it yellow on command.

2) The rain? Not so much. If I wanted to get wet, I'd chase ducks into a lake, thanks. Now, if splashing through a rain puddle suddenly counts as my bath, I'll make an exception, but my humans aren't very keen on multitasking when it comes to hygiene. Hey, their time to waste, not mine!

3) Thunder is *awful*. I think it was designed just to scare me. Not cool. I don't need to hear any more of that, ever.

Thanks,
Bailey

Hi Santa,

I'm told that my hugs are amazing—and I don't even know how to hug. Explain that one!

You definitely look like you could use a hug tonight. I'm sorry I haven't mastered the mechanics of hugging back, but I promise that if you throw your arms around me and squeeze you will instantly feel better about the long night ahead of you.

Shannon

Dear Santa,

If shoes aren't meant to be eaten, then humans shouldn't keep leaving them on the floor. Has the entire world gone *mad?*

Why am I the one with crushed-up crazy pills sprinkled over my kibble? Please bring *them* the pills!

Your friend,
Gary

DEAR SANTA,

Having the cat around was bad enough, but this other guy you brought us last Christmas, "Roomba"? He's just AWFUL.

He's loud, but I can't understand anything he says. He snatches up all of the crumbs from underneath the kitchen table and won't share them with me. Also, I think he's blind and too stuck-up to admit it. He crashes into everything, but he won't let me give him directions. He just backs up and keeps wandering aimlessly around the house.

Please do me a favor this Christmas: Take him back to whatever terrible planet he came from. I promise it will be our secret.

Thank you,
Winston

Hi Santa,

So you're telling me there were supposed to be *cookies* on this plate but somebody ate them?

I think you must be mistaken. Our holiday tradition is to leave Santa a glass of milk with a *button* we found under the couch. Sorry for the confusion.

Espy

DEAR SANTA,

For Christmas I would like lots of cans of premium, top-shelf cat food.

Actually, who am I kidding? Anything that gets put in the cat's dish will automatically trump whatever is in mine.

Thank you,
Gilda

Dear Santa,

How come when the humans sing it's called karaoke, but when I sing it's called "Shut up, Sammy!"

I don't see them signing any record contracts, do you? Two can play this game—please bring me the largest earmuffs you can find.

Your friend,
Sammy

Dear Santa,

If humans should "stop and smell the roses," then what's so wrong about my stopping to smell every tree (and curb and hydrant and trash can and butt) on my walks? It seems awfully hypocritical for my human to get bent out of shape when I'm clearly the more spiritually evolved one.

Maybe after you drop off the presents this Christmas you could hide her phone and her watch—it's for her own good.

Your friend,
Daffy

Dear Santa,

I don't want to alarm you, but there is some dark magic afoot. Let me (very carefully) walk you through it:

- Total fences around the yard that I can see: zero
- Total fences around the yard the humans see: zero
- Total fences the small humans see: zero (you get the picture)

So how come when everyone *else* leaves the yard, they don't get the Charles Dickens shocked out of them and *I* do?

Since you are also magical, I'm hoping you have the ability to see this terrible fence and can cut it down on my behalf before I really, *really* lose my marbles.

Thank you,
Baby Ruth

Dear Santa,

If the scuttlebutt around here is to be believed, I am a "herder."

The good news is that I am always up for the task. Nothing gives me more pure, type A satisfaction than putting people and things in their rightful place.

The bad news is that those other layabouts at the dog run don't share my enthusiasm and seem far more consumed with sniffing backsides than forming tidy groups based on breed, color, and size.

Can you spare a herd of sheep? How about dogs who act like sheep?

Sincerely,
Duchess

HI SANTA,

Who among us can resist the tipped-over trash can's haunting siren song?

Well okay, good for you . . . but can you still help me pick up all of this scattered trash so I won't get in trouble on Christmas morning? Pretty, pretty please?

Sookie

DEAR SANTA,

I'm so excited for Christmas and can't wait for your visit! Just checking—are you allergic to dogs? Sneezes are VERY SCARY. I want to be prepared if I have to suddenly tear out of the room, and I don't want you to be offended.

Thank you for understanding. Also, there's a box of tissues on the coffee table.

Your friend,
Mama

DEAR SANTA,

My humans are really bumming me out lately with their barbs about my "dangerous weight" and "special food" (which tastes like garbage, by the way, and *not* the delicious kind).

Have they ever considered that instead of me getting smaller, the doggie door could stand to be bigger? Even a hamster would panic trying to hurl itself through that thing.

Besides, your weight doesn't stop you from jumping down millions of chimneys each Christmas Eve, and you even get rewarded with cookies. Thank you for being an inspiration, Santa.

Keep fighting the good fight!

Love,
Muffin

P.S. Could you sneak me a few slices of bacon?

DEAR SANTA,

Dogs are not meant to be schlepped around town in purses. Please bring me a stroller for Christmas.

Love,
Roy

DEAR SANTA,

Can you bring me some Band-Aids?

Fair warning: When the cat wags her tail, it does NOT mean the same thing as when I wag my tail.

Your pal,
Louie

Hi Santa,

Hello from the den! Over here, Santa, here I am! Sorry to yell.

Oh, this gate—this gate that I'm stuck behind, you mean? It's to keep the baby out. Yes, it's definitely for the baby. He's somewhere around here.

Now that I'm thinking about it, since it's so late he must be sound asleep. Would you mind taking the gate down? I feel so rude yelling across the house. As soon as I'm closer to you and the presents, you can put it right back up, of course.

Loretta

DEAR SANTA,

Booties. Even the name lacks dignity.

Please don't bring me more. I'm running out of hiding spots for them around the house. And trust me—my pride is way more sensitive than my paws.

Sincerely,
P-nut

DEAR SANTA,

For Christmas, can you please bring an extra plush dog bed . . . for the cat? It might seem confusing, but we've got a pretty neat system worked out here. Nobody sleeps in the cat's bed; the cat sleeps in my bed, and I sleep in my humans' bed. Everybody's happy!

I guess it does get kind of crowded in the big bed (especially when the cat mixes things up and wants to sleep with our humans, too . . . that happens a lot, actually), but, like the song says, we are family!

Best wishes,
Samba

Dear Santa,

If the Internet is to be believed, I already know how to skateboard and how to surf, even though I've never tried either activity in my life.

I would like one board for each, please!

Your friend,
Trixie

Dear Santa,

This is a little awkward . . . would you mind bringing me a menorah and eight extra presents? I keep trying to tell my humans that I'm Jewish, but they aren't taking the hint.

Thanks,
Java

Hi Santa,

Who's being a butt? WHO'S BEING A BUTT?
No, really . . . who?

Clyde

HI SANTA,

Look, I found a way to make it snow inside—
Merry Christmas!

On a related note, I hope you have lots of
pillows and stuffed animals in that bag for us.
Otherwise I'll be in a heap of trouble tomorrow
morning.

Lila

DEAR SANTA,

My Christmas list is attached.

Before you type my address into your sleigh's
GPS, though, I want to assure you: I'm telling the
truth! I really DO live on a farm upstate!

Love,
Mookie

Dear Santa,

While you're distributing toys around the world, would you mind passing out these head shots? A couple thousand per country is fine.

I just know that somebody somewhere will see one and immediately recognize me as their perfect team mascot. The sport isn't important. All that matters is that I already possess the three Cs: charm, class, and *crazy* amounts of energy!
Go team!

Love,
Jackson

Dear Santa,

OMG, OMG, BUBBLES!!
    I love bubbles, bubbles, bubbles, BUBBLES!
    Pop, pop, pop,
    POP!

                          Your friend,
                          Taco

Hi Santa!

Oh, the cat? If I know the cat, she's off sleeping somewhere, *again*. I'm happy to hold all of her presents for her in the meantime. It's no trouble at all, honest!

Sugar

Dear Santa,

Please find attached 1,365 selfies I snapped over the past few months. I just know my humans are going to love next year's "a Dusty a day" calendar.

Thanks so much for your help. I wanted to give you lots of options, which is why there are some extras.

What can I say—the camera loves me!

Your friend,
Dusty

Dear Santa,

How fast can your reindeer fly? I'll bet superfast!

How about you guys take me for a quick spin around the neighborhood? I'm sure your presents take up lots of space, but don't worry—I'll save room by keeping my head outside the sleigh the whole time.

Wheeeeeee!

ET

Dear Santa,

Please bring us more rolls of toilet paper. I got a little carried away with "decking the halls" with them.

Sincerely,
Amos

Hi Santa,

I know you have a busy night ahead of you, but . . . my leash is right by the chimney, and I could really, *really* go for some fresh air.

I would hate to bark and wake up the whole house and blow your cover. Wouldn't it be awful if Christmas was RUINED?

I'll meet you by the door!

Norton

DEAR SANTA,

Wearing this cone is the pits. At least I've discovered a fun party trick:

If you toss me a dog biscuit with just the right amount of spin and momentum in your throw, the dog biscuit will circle around and around the cone before it lands in my mouth, like a coin in a funnel—but way more fun!

It takes a LOT of tries to perfect. Luckily there's an economy-size box of biscuits right near the Christmas tree. We should probably start practicing right away.

Sincerely,
Rupert

Dear Santa,

I work hard every day, wouldn't you agree? Keeping tabs on my tail, jumping up and down in front of the window for the mailman, and finding the perfect boot for stowing my rawhide bone are all incredibly taxing—and that's before noon!

Ergo, I don't think putting the peanut butter right on my tongue every once in a while is too much to ask.

No, I would *not* like to spend an additional three hours digging it out of that thingy, thank you very much. Can you set a good example for my humans this Christmas by putting an open jar of peanut butter right on the floor? I would really appreciate it.

Your friend,
Babu

Dear Santa,

Can you remind me how many Iditarod races your reindeer have won? I've been on winning dogsled teams for four years running (fast—ha!) now. Or is it five years? They kind of blur together.

Are you sure the reindeer are the best candidates to pull your sleigh? Is the dependable, scenic route really better than traveling in half the amount of time?

Sincerely,
Pepé

P.S. My business card is enclosed; sleep on it, and feel free to contact me any time.

Dear Santa,

I have accepted that my humans will not let me
have even the ittiest, bittiest piece of chocolate
(sigh), so it's pointless for me to ask for some.

However, in the interest of having a well-
rounded resume, please know that I would like to
pursue all of my gummy, taffy, jelly, cookie, and
snack cake options to the fullest extent this
Christmas.

Your friend,
Otis

Dear Santa,

I'll admit that I looked pretty adorable in the reindeer antlers my humans put on me for the family Christmas card picture. I was a good sport about wearing them during the tree trimming and for the Christmas party, too.

But it has been three weeks, Santa. WE GET IT: I'm a reindeer—har, har, har.

And now I'm a reindeer with a migraine. Would you be a pal when you visit us and take these things off my head?

Yours,
Sophie

Dear Santa,

You want to know what *really* stinks? I didn't even invite the dog with the white stripe into our yard. He just wandered over. Of course I still sniffed his butt, to be polite, but how could I have known how angry this would make him? His reaction was extremely uncalled for.

Now my humans keep cursing and covering their noses and acting like this whole thing was *my* fault. Meanwhile, I've never seen so many tomatoes in one bathtub.

Bring us more, if you must. I just thought you should hear my side of the story.

Best,
Harlem

DEAR SANTA,

Confession time: Do you know where all the humans' missing socks really end up? My belly.

Enclosed are all of the socks missing a mate— thanks for replacing them! If you could do me a solid by shoving them in the dryer, it would take the heat off me by perpetuating their "mischievous elves" theory. No offense to your elves, of course, who I am sure are all very honest and hardworking.

Your pal,
Clay

DEAR SANTA,

Oh, sure, from the outside it must seem like I have it all: perfectly manicured nails; a luxurious coat so shiny that the judges have to wear sunglasses during my graceful laps around the winner's circle; fresh breath; and, of course, six "best of breed" ribbons to hammer all of this superiority home.

But Santa, can I tell you a secret? On the inside I am miserable—an empty husk of a Husky. I don't want to be a dog at these dog and pony shows any longer (where are the ponies?). I don't want to keep preening for the cameras.

Can I tell you another secret? What I really, *really* want to do is . . . paint. Do you think you could sneak me some paints and brushes? But please hide them carefully! My humans don't tolerate my artistic flair. They don't want me to follow my bliss. But I know *you* do, Santa!

Sincerely,
Georgie

P.S. You didn't ask, but I'm thinking portraits of humans will be my sweet spot.

HI SANTA,

It's okay, I won't blow your cover. Sure, "presents," yadda, yadda, I know the drill.

Let's level: You lift the lid off the cat's litter box, no questions asked, and quietly walk away. I never saw you, and YOU never saw ME—capiche?

Izzy

DEAR SANTA,

My human should love those new sneakers you brought, but if possible, I'd like a few minutes alone with the old ones before you chuck them in the Dumpster out back.

Happy trails, stinky friends (the sneakers—not you and the reindeer)!

Best wishes,
Grover

Dear Santa,

Will you please help fund my upcoming project? It's tentatively titled *Shifting Paradigms: Dogs Rule and Cats Drool*. I'm still not sure if it's going to be a book, a documentary, or maybe modern art. I *do* know that it's going to challenge norms and set the world on fire.

And you can help make it happen, Santa! If you pledge $20, I will send you a tote bag and add you to my mailing list.

Your friend,
Maggie

Dear Santa,

Gadzooks, somebody stole all of the pizza crusts I was saving between the couch cushions!

I'll need to replenish my supply immediately. Please bring me at least six large pizzas and a helper to polish off all but the crusts for each. Know of any jolly, bearded men with healthy appetites who might be up to the task? Wink, wink!

Your friend,
Bert

Dear Santa,

A leash for the cat! Why didn't I think of it sooner?
No wonder she's so cranky all the time—nobody
ever takes her on walks.

Her own leash will mean we can spend a lot
more quality time together. I have a good feeling
about this.

Love,
Buddha

Hi Santa,

Is that my present?

Drop it. Drop it. DROP IT, Santa! RIGHT
THIS MINUTE!

Cleo

Dear Santa,

If the sofa isn't for Lumpy to sleep on, why is it there? Why is it such a comfy place for Lumpy to turn around and around in circles before curling up into a ball and sinking down into the cushions? Who decided to make the pillows so delicious?

It's one big, cozy trap, if you ask Lumpy.

No more games. If Lumpy doesn't get to be on the sofa, no one gets to be on the sofa—could you please haul it away before Christmas morning?

Sincerely,
Lumpy

P.S. Lumpy would help you carry it out of the house . . . but Lumpy's back isn't so great.

DEAR SANTA,

Can you bring me some oil for my back wheels?
They're getting a bit squeaky.

Also, a strand of Christmas lights to string
around them would really boost my holiday cheer.

Thank you,
Oliver

Dear Santa,

For years whenever my humans insisted "you have to take the stairs, Rosie," I naively believed them—like a chump.

So how can they explain what I saw on the TV last night? There was a man *riding a chair* on the stairs. He didn't have to do anything except press a button, and it carried him all the way up and then all the way back down.

I would very much like one of these magic chairs. But please make sure this one is "Rosie size" and not "lying human" size.

Thanks,
Rosie

Hi Santa!

I hear you . . . mm-hmm . . . mm-hmm . . . sure
. . . mm-hmm . . . yup . . . mm-hmm . . . mm-hmm
. . . oh, absolutely!

Wait, can you repeat all that? Sorry. It
probably seemed like I was listening, since my
head was cocked to the side, but I was actually
daydreaming about a churro I once ate.

Goldie

DEAR SANTA,

Is there anything sadder than a squeaky toy that has lost its squeaker?

That was a rhetorical question. I'm obviously going to need a bunch of new squeaky toys for Christmas.

Your friend,
Hank

P.S. Also, the baby's squeaker is defective and stuck on the "scream" setting. Please recall her model and send us a new baby with a functional squeaker.

Dear Santa,

The fellas and I are pretty excited you'll finally get to hear our barbershop quartet. We've been practicing every night this month. I'm on lead vocals and our tenor, Bubba, lives next door; Toby, our baritone, is about two blocks away; rounding us out on bass somewhere else in the neighborhood is Chester, the most majestically piped Saint Bernard you'll ever faintly hear.

Apologies that we haven't quite mastered Christmas carols yet. But I'm confident that our rendition of "Sweet Adeline" will move you to tears again and again (it's the only song we know) and again.

Your friends,
Barry and the Bow Wow Howlers

Dear Santa,

I would like some hot dogs for Christmas, but I just had a terrible epiphany: There will never be enough hot dogs for me to eat. You can bring me some hot dogs, but then I will eat them and they will be gone. I will then want more hot dogs. Once those hot dogs arrive, I will eat them, and they will also be gone, and I will want more hot dogs.

Kind of makes you question the whole point of this endless merry-go-round, doesn't it?

Sorry to be a bummer. I'm going to go chew through some cables. That always makes me feel better.

Sincerely,
Nova

Hi Santa,

A little higher . . . little higher . . . okay, now a little lower . . . lower . . . higher again . . . almost . . . yeah, yeah, yeah, RIGHT THERE! THAT'S the stuff!

Your head scratches are all aces.

Snickers

Dear Santa,

Every year I hope my humans will finally extend my zip line from the backyard into the front yard, and every year I'm disappointed. I think this year you'll have to help me take matters into my own paws.

I can't wait to see their expressions when they look out the window and see me in the driveway on Christmas morning. A giant red bow for my head would also be a nice touch.

Your friend,
Brandy

DEAR SANTA,

Here is a complimentary copy of my new album, *Careless Whistles*. Enjoy!

Your friend,
Sidney

P.S. It's not blank; it was just recorded at a frequency most humans can't hear. You might have to take my word for it.

Hi Santa,

Be honest: Would YOU wear this sweater?

Hannah

Dear Santa,

I'm sorry I freaked out on you last Christmas. In hindsight, the Christmas tree was nowhere near my food bowl. It sort of seemed like you were walking toward the food bowl, though. Or at least you were looking in the direction of the food bowl and thinking about walking toward it.

This Christmas I'll try to keep my paranoia in check.

Sincerely,
Casper

P.S. You don't want to steal my food bowl . . . right?

DEAR SANTA,

Taco here again:

I apologize for my curtness in the last two letters. I hope I didn't come off rudely. I was simply distracted by—

Squirrel! Squirrel! Squirrel! Squirrel!

There he is, there he is, there he is, OH MAN, OH MAN, OH MANohmanohman—

Up the tree.

I'm very sorry. What was I saying?

Regards,
Taco

Dear Santa,

No Gift Left Wrapped: my motto, my mission, my life's work. Your generous donations will provide a joyful day of frenzied paper tearing (and maybe a little gastrointestinal drama later on, but that's hardly your fault).

Your tax receipt is by the eggnog.

With gratitude,
Oscar

Dear Santa,

For Christmas I would like you to bring us the
Ding Dong D-Lux 3000.

The ad says it has more than fifty unique
doorbell rings. I'm barking just thinking about all
of them!

Thank you,
Peony

Hi Santa,

Oh, look! Mistletoe!

Rules are rules. Your face isn't gonna lick
itself for ten minutes straight, is it?

Lux

Wait . . . Santa?

Where are you going? Are you leaving me?

No, Santa!

No! No! No!

This is literally the WORST thing that has ever happened to me. I am BROKEN. I am NEVER moving from this corner. NOPE. I will wait here for an entire year until you come back to me.

Hey . . . is that a new bone over there?

A NEW BONE???

MY LIFE IS GLORIOUS!!

BEST. CHRISTMAS. EVER.

Monty